MURPHY

THE WONDER DOG

MURPHY
THE WONDER DOG

Harold Town

 **MOSAIC PRESS**
OAKVILLE NEW YORK LONDON

CANADIAN CATALOGUING IN PUBLICATION DATA

Town, Harold, 1924 –
    Murphy the wonder dog

ISBN 0-88962-293-0

1. Dogs — Juvenile fiction. I. Title.

PS8589.095M87 1985   jC813'.54   C85-099617-1
PZ10.3.T68Mu 1985

Published by Mosaic Press, P.O. Box 1032, Oakville, Ontario, L6J 5E9, Canada. Offices and warehouse at 1252 Speers Road, Unit 10, Oakville, Ontario, L6L 5N9, Canada.

Published with the assistance of the Canada Council and the Ontario Arts Council.

Copyright © Harold Town, 1987.
Designed by Rita Vogel.
Typeset by Lount Graphics.
Printed and bound in Hong Kong

ISBN 0-88962-293-0 cloth

MOSAIC PRESS:

In the United States: Riverrun Press Inc., 1170 Broadway, Suite 807, New York, N.Y., 10000, USA.

In the U.K.: John Calder (Publishers) Ltd., 18 Brewer Street, London, W1R 4AS, England.

Dogs are never more attractive than when, with the stillness that seems to go beyond time, they concentrate on master or foe.

In these moments, intense and nearly guileless, they are as complete as rocks about to explode in the desert sun, and seem to hark back to an age when life was not just a series of distractions, but one huge, powerful event.

MURPHY THE WONDER DOG

6

observing the dog days of August

MURPHY THE WONDER DOG

observing a naughty dog turning to stones

MURPHY THE WONDER DOG

observing the first walking mushrooms

MURPHY THE WONDER DOG

observing that there are no dogs in a doggeral

MURPHY THE WONDER DOG

observing the first swimming rock

MURPHY THE WONDER DOG

observing the first earth blister

MURPHY THE WONDER DOG

observing the first floating jube jube

MURPHY THE WONDER DOG

observing giants looking at the moon

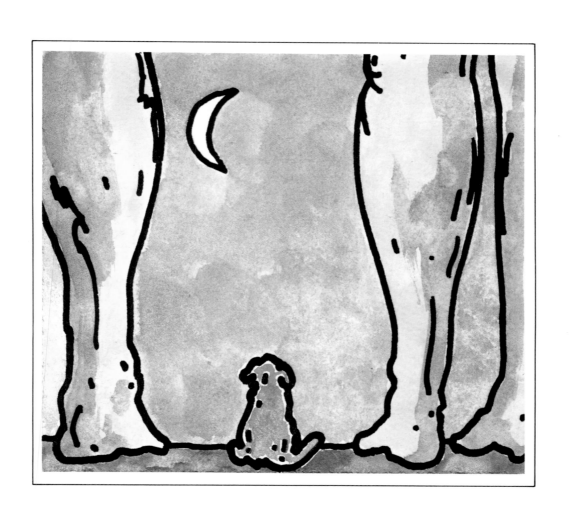

MURPHY THE WONDER DOG

observing the first flying tree

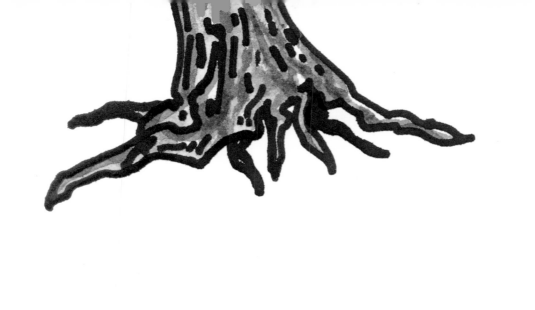

MURPHY THE WONDER DOG

observing the first oblong clouds

MURPHY THE WONDER DOG

observing a spider spinning a chair

MURPHY THE WONDER DOG

observing the first knitting smoke

MURPHY THE WONDER DOG

observing information crossing a desk

MURPHY THE WONDER DOG

observing the first earth to sky lightning

MURPHY THE WONDER DOG

observing that the tomb of the unknown dog is in questionable taste